S0-EAU-797

FINGER PLAY FUN

Violette G. Steiner

Roberta Evatt Pond

Charles E. Merrill Publishing Co.
A Bell & Howell Company
Columbus, Ohio

International Standard Book Number: 0-675-09312-0

Library of Congress Catalog Card Number:

2 3 4 5 6 7 8 9 10 / 75 74 74 73 72

Printed in the United States of America

PREFACE

Here is a collection of old and new finger plays in a version especially designed to help children's language development. Finger plays, like any other form of good literature, have a quality of timelessnes; they have been a delight to children of all nations in all eras. They have helped children learn to listen with purpose, to use language, and to be aware of the quality of rhyming words. They act as springboards to help children learn to enjoy poetry and literature and to understand the world in which they live.

Learning about language starts as soon as a child is born; the child learns to clap his hands and to have fun with language long before he can repeat the words. What parent has not helped her little one, cooed and talked to him, played "patty-cake" or "This Little Pig"? Simple little things, but important for continuing language development. Finger plays give a child his first contact with literature long before he knows the meaning of words. They also provide the word repetition which he loves and needs while in the process of learning language. This repetition is also one of the charms of finger plays. Moreover, they help children learn to love language, to have fun with words, to communicate with others, and to begin to develop a sense of humor.

This book would have been ten books if it tried to present every finger play that is a part of our rich folklore. The ones collected here were selected because they are the favorites of the many children whom we have known and loved.

Finger Play Fun has been designed with a three-fold purpose in mind. First, it provides teachers and parents with material for stimulating language development in young children. Secondly, the material in each chapter has been carefully arranged according to the interest level and verbal ability of children approximately two to six years of age. Finally, and most important, it is designed for children to have fun with language and with YOU.

This book is presented

to

____

With love,

from

____

CONTENTS

ACKNOWLEDGEMENTS

Grateful acknowledgement is made to the following for their contributions to this book.

For taking the photographs:

Mr. Keith Eby
Mr. Steven Wood

For line drawings:

Miss Janet Snyder
Mr. Stan Niemi
Mr. Greig Steiner

For permission to reprint poems:

Florence Burns, "The Stilt Man", in *Creative Rhytmic Movement for Children,* by Gladys Andrews, Englewood Cliffs, N.J.: Prentice-Hall, Inc., 1954.

Vachel Lindsay, "The Little Turtle", *Collected Poems,* New York: The Macmillan Company, 1925.

For permission to use pictures of their equipment:

County of Los Angeles Fire Department

Union Pacific Railroad Company

For permission to use photographs of their children and/or themselves:

Mrs. Meredith Ashbaugh
Mrs. Anita Barefield
Mrs. Mary Lynn Butcher
Mrs. Barbara Chandler
Mrs. Arlene Christensen
Mrs. Karen Davis
Mrs. Nancy Garrow
Mrs. Eva Goforth
Mrs. Priscilla Hansen
Mrs. Patricia Hardi
Mrs. Hope Herrera
Mrs. Rachel Holliday
Mrs. Wanda Howser
Capt. Earl Kramer
Mrs. Janelle Kupke
Mrs. Frances Levison
Mr. R. S. Mitchell
Mrs. Bridie Morgan
Mrs. Darlane Morone
Mrs. Joan Munoz
Mrs. Ruth Nelson
Mrs. Evelyn Penrose
Mrs. LaVerne Popham
Mrs. K. Ragsdale
Mrs. Carmen Shook
Mrs. Ethel Smith
Mrs. J. M. Steiner
Mrs. Mary Frances Sullens
Mrs. Vitia Suter
Mrs. Linda Velte
Mrs. Rita Watkins
Mrs. Shirley Yates

TIPS FOR ADULTS

Choose rhymes *you* think will be fun to do with a child.

Choose ones that are within his memory ability.

Choose ones which will interest him.

Build yourself a large repertoire.

Children love to listen and to *do!*

Children love to repeat, and repeat, and repeat, and repeat, and repeat finger plays!

Have fun! Have fun! Have fun!

FINGER PLAY FUN

CHAPTER I QUIET TIME

Sometimes I like to quiet be,

And sit and have you read to me.

Then I'm happy to hear you say,

"Come, let's do a finger play."

CREEPING INDIANS

The Indians are creeping,
(creep fingers along forearm)

Shh . . . . . Shh . . . . . Shh . . . . .
(raise fingers to lips)

The Indians are creeping,
(creep fingers along forearm)

Shh . . . . . Shh . . . . . Shh . . . . .
(raise fingers to lips)

They do not make a sound

As their feet touch the ground.

The Indians are creeping,
(creep fingers along forearm)

Shh . . . . . Shh . . . . . Shh . . . . .
(raise fingers to lips)

OPEN THEM, SHUT THEM

Open them, shut them; open them, shut them;
(open and close hands)

Give your hands a clap.
(clap hands)

Shut them, open them; shut them, open them;
(shut and open hands)

Fold them in your lap.
(hands in lap)

THIS LITTLE GIRL

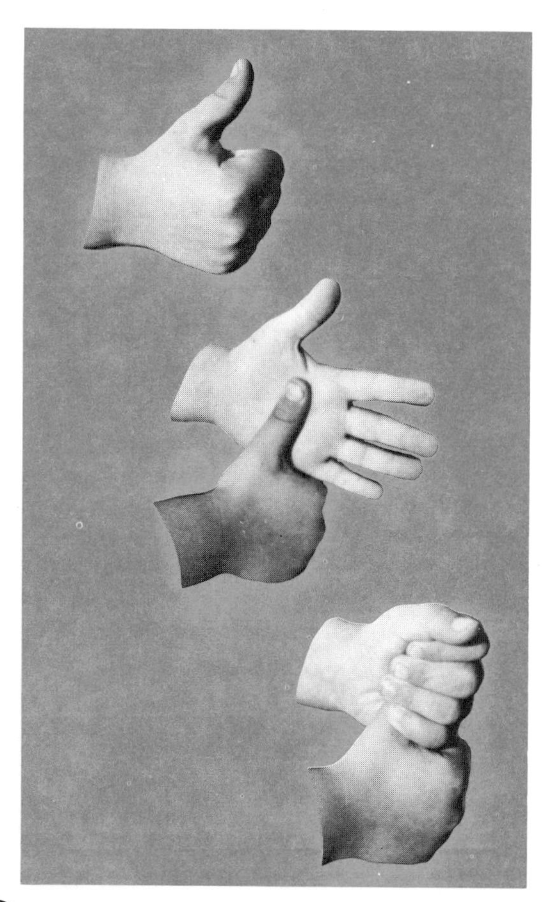

This little girl is ready for bed,
(hold up thumb)

Down on the pillow she lays her head.
(put thumb across palm of other hand)

Wraps herself in covers so tight,
(close fingers over thumb)

And this is the way she sleeps all night.
(put hands up to cheek and close eyes)

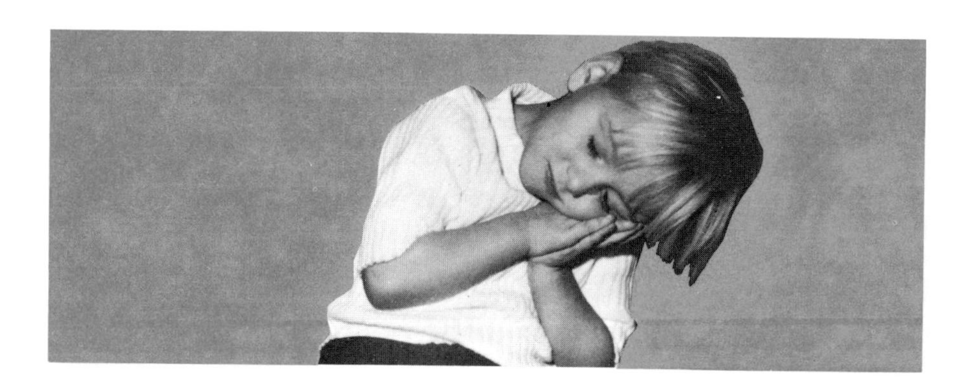

GRANDMOTHER

Here are grandmother's glasses,
(make glasses with thumb and finger)

This is grandmother's hat.
(make hat with hands)

This is the way she folds her hands,
(fold hands gently)

And puts them in her lap.
(lay them in lap)

Here are grandpa's spectacles,
(make larger circle with thumb and index finger and place over eyes)

And here is grandpa's hat.
(make larger pointed hat, as above)

And here is the way he folds his arms,
(fold arms with vigor)

Just like that!

MY FINGERS

I have ten little fingers
(follow action as rhyme indicates)

And they all belong to me.

Would you like to see?

I can shut them up tight.

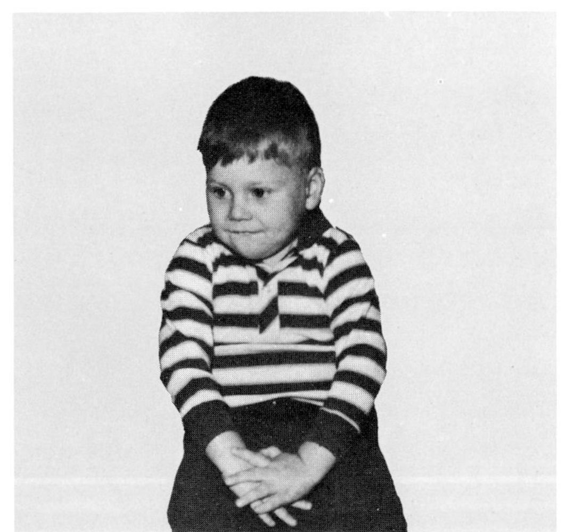

Or open them wide.

I can put them together,

Or make them all hide.

I can make them jump high,

I can make them jump low,

I can fold them quietly,

And hold them just so.

QUIET BE

Let your hands clap, clap, clap;
(clap hands three times)

Let your fingers tap, tap, tap.
(tap fingers three times)

Fold your arms and quiet be,
(fold arms)

Roll your hands so wide awake.
(roll hands)

Let your fingers shake, shake, shake.
(shake fingers)

Climb the ladder; do not fall,
(hold hands open, palms down; step one over the other, high above head)

Till we reach the steeple tall.
(hands make steeple)

Fold your hands and quiet be.
(fold hands)

TWO THIEVING MICE

Two thieving mice went stealing through the house,
(extend index and middle finger of each hand)

Shh . . shh . . shh . . said the first little mouse,
(middle and index fingers of left hand open and close to portray sound)

Achoo, achoo, achoo, sneezed his very noisy wife.
(middle and index finger of right hand open and close to portray sound)

Shh . . shh . . shh . . do you want to lose your life?
(left fingers move as in first instruction)

Achoo, achoo, achoo, this cold may kill me dead,
(right fingers move as in second instruction)

Shh . . shh . . shh . . or the cat will have your head!
(left fingers move as in first instruction)

Achoo, achoo, achoo, oh, I'd better go to bed.
(right fingers move as in second instruction)

BUSY FINGERS

(Also can be sung to "Here We Go Round the Mulberry Bush")

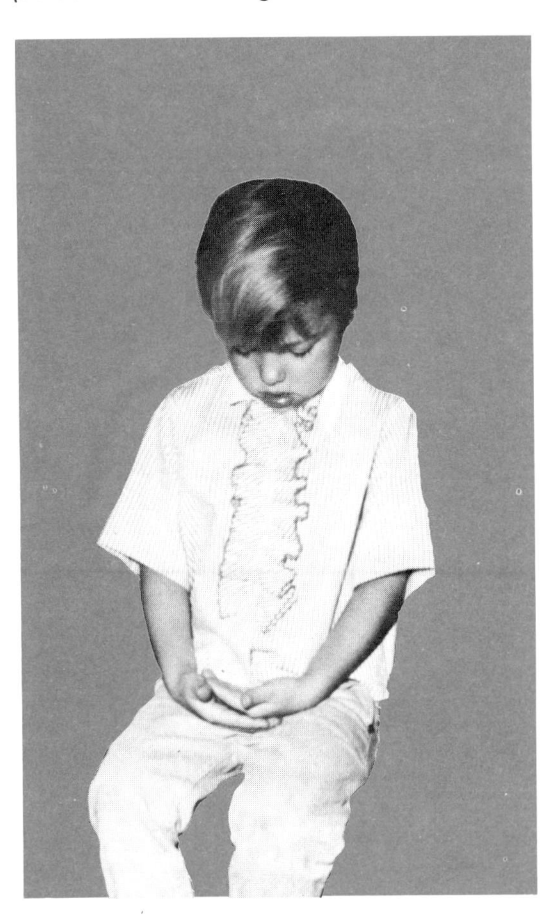

This is the way my fingers stand, fingers stand, fingers stand,
(follow action as rhyme indicates)

This is the way my fingers stand, so early in the morning.
(hold fingers out straight)

This is the way they dance about, dance about, dance about,

This is the way they dance about, so early in the morning.

This is the way I fold my hands, fold my hands, fold my hands,

This is the way I fold my hands, so early in the morning.

This is the way they go to rest, go to rest, go to rest,
(cup hands loosely, palms up, and place in lap)

This is the way they go to rest, so early in the morning.

WIGGLE WORM

Do you always have to wiggle?
(wiggle in the chair)

Do you always have to squirm?

You wiggle and you jiggle,
(wiggle and jiggle)

Like a regular wiggle worm.
(use hand to make wiggly motion)

You wiggle in your chair,
(wiggle in your chair)

And you wiggle in your bed.

You wiggle with your legs,
(wiggle legs)

And you wiggle with your head.
(shake head)

You wiggle with your hands,
(shake hands)

And you wiggle with your feet.
(move feet)

You wiggle when you're playing,

And you wiggle when you eat.

I guess you're made to wiggle,
(everyone wiggle)

And I guess you're made to squirm,

So I'll like the wiggle-jiggle,

And I'll love my wiggle worm.

DROWSY

A drowsy head is nodding,
(nod head)

A pair of eyes are blinking.
(blink eyes)

This child is ready for bed,
(fold hands together)

I'm thinking.
(place hands under cheek)

CHAPTER II COUNTING

Numbers will tell me how much or how many,

And how much candy I'll get for a penny.

I can count up to twenty, but that's far as I'll go,

Because that's when I've used every finger and toe!

HOT CROSS BUNS

Hot cross buns,
(clap hands in rhythm or make cross on palm)

Hot cross buns,

One a-penny, two a-penny,
(count out two fingers)

Hot cross buns.

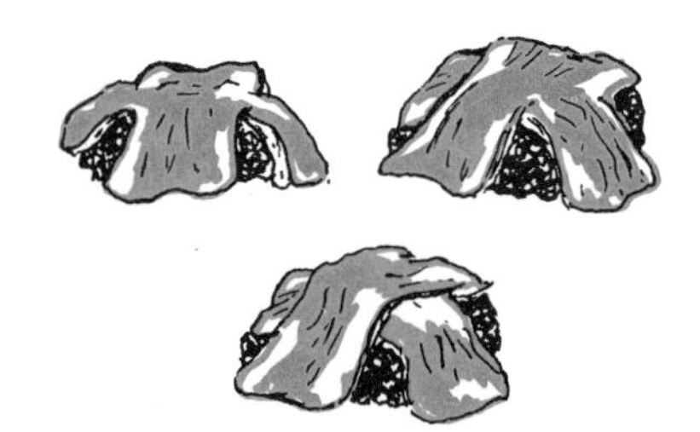

ONE, TWO, BUCKLE MY SHOE

One, two, buckle my shoe;
(follow action as rhyme indicates)

Three, four, knock at the door;

Five, six, pick up sticks;

Seven, eight, lay them straight;

Nine, ten, a big fat hen.
((extend hands, finger tips touching)

EENY, MEENY, MINEY, MO

Eeny, meeny, miney, mo;
(point to each finger)

Catch a tiger by the toe;
(hold one finger with other hand)

When he hollers let him go.
(let go of finger)

Eeny, meeny, miney, mo.
(point to each finger again)

(For counting out, point to each child in turn. Vary pointing by tapping shoes, etc.)

THIS LITTLE PIG

This little pig went to market,
(hold one finger at a time as you say the poem)

This little pig stayed home,

This little pig had roast beef,

This little pig had none,

This little pig cried, "Wee, wee, wee!"

All the way home.

BALLS

A great big ball,
(make a big ball with arms)

A middle-sized ball,
(make smaller ball)

A little ball, I see.
(make a little ball with hands)

I guess I'll count them,

One, two, three.
(make balls as you count)

ONE FOR THE MONEY

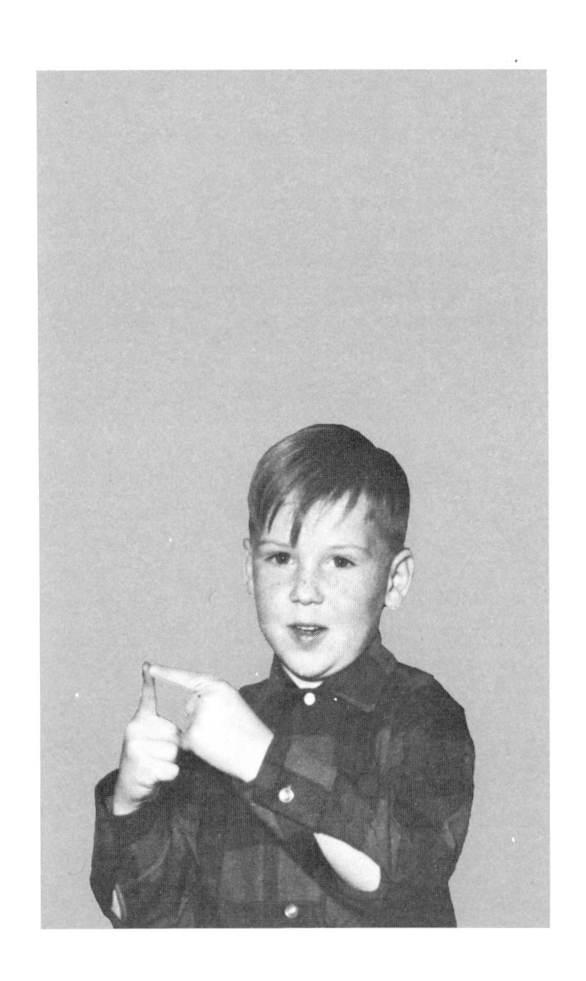

One for the money,
(point to each finger)

Two for the show,

Three to get ready,

And four to go.

BEE HIVES

Here are the bee hives,
(left hand cupped upward)

Where are the bees?

Hidden away where nobody sees.
(hide fingers of right hand in left)

Soon they will come creeping
(fingers creep out)

Out of the hive.

One, two, three, four, five, "Buzzz z zzzzzzzz."
(fingers fly away)

LITTLE ELEPHANTS

One, two, three, four, five,
(count fingers)

Five little elephants standing in a row.

This little elephant stubbed his toe,
(point to each finger in turn)

This little elephant said, "Oh, oh, oh,"

This little elephant laughed and was glad,

This little elephant cried and was sad,

This little elephant so thoughtful and good,

He ran for the doctor as fast as he could.

BUNNIES

"My bunnies now must go to bed,"
(left hand up, fingers straight)

The little mother rabbit said.
(hold up right fist, index finger up)

"But I will count them first to see,

If they have all come back to me."

"One bunny, two bunnies, three bunnies dear,
(touch the fingers in turn as you count)

Four bunnies, five bunnies — yes, all are here!

They are the prettiest things alive —

My bunnies, one, two, three, four, five."
(again touch fingers as you count)

FIVE LITTLE DUCKS

Five little ducks went in for a swim;
(hold up hand, extend fingers)

The first little duck put his head in.
(point to each finger in turn)

The second little duck put his head back;

The third little duck said, "Quack, quack, quack."

The fourth little duck with his tiny brother,

Went for a walk with his father and mother.
("walk" fingers up opposite arm)

BLUEBIRDS

Five little bluebirds and no more,
(hold up hand, fingers extended)

One flew away and then there were four.
(fold down one finger as each bird flies away)

Four little bluebirds sitting in a tree;

One flew away and then there were three.

Three little bluebirds looking at you;

One flew away and then there were two.

Two little bluebirds sitting in the sun;

One flew away and then there was one.

One little bluebird sitting all alone;

He flew away and then there was none.

FIVE LITTLE CLOWNS

Five little clowns running through a door,
(hold up one hand, fingers extended)

One fell down and then there were four.
(tuck one finger in palm for each line until all make a fist)

Four little clowns in an apple tree;

One fell out, and then there were three.

Three little clowns stirring up some stew;

One fell in, and then there were two.

Two little clowns having lots of fun;

One ran away, and then there was one.

One little clown left sitting in the sun;

He went home, and then there was none.

FIVE LITTLE FROGS

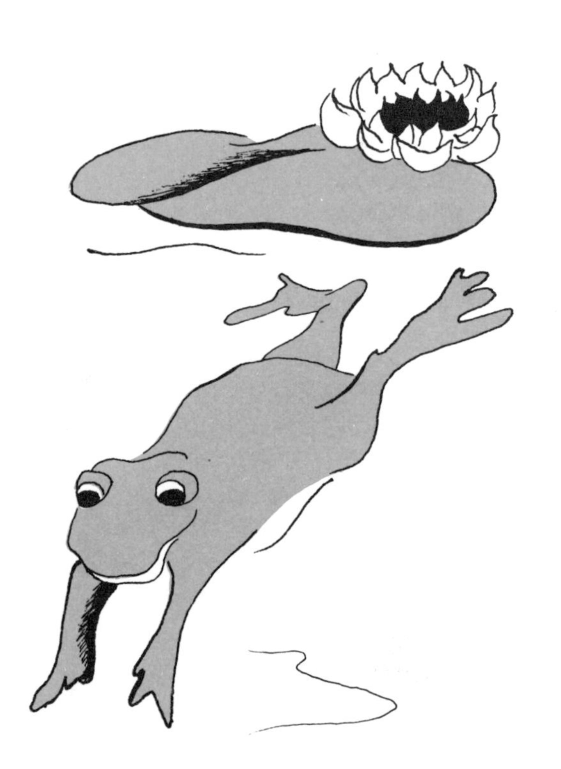

Five little frogs sat on the shore,

(open hand, extend fingers, push down one finger as each frog leaves)

One went for a swim and then there were four.

Four little frogs, and then there were three.

Three little frogs said, "What can we do?"

One jumped in the water and then there were two.

Two little frogs sat in the sun,

One swam off, and then there was one.

One lonely frog said, "This is no fun."

He dived into the water, and then there was none.

CATCHING A FISH

One, two, three, four, five,
(count out fingers on right hand)

I caught a little fish alive.
(catch all fingers on right hand with left hand)

Six, seven, eight, nine, ten,
(count out fingers on left hand)

I let it go again.
(hands fly apart suddenly)

Why did you let it go?

Because it bit my finger so.
(shake right hand)

Which finger did it bite?

The little finger on the right.
(point to little finger on right hand)

FIVE LITTLE SOLDIERS

Five little soldiers standing in a row,
(hold up fingers of one hand)

Three stood straight,
(hold three fingers straight)

And two stood so.
(bend two fingers)

Along came the captain,
(extend index finger on other hand and move in front of first hand)

And what do you think?

They all stood straight, as quick as a wink.
(hold all five fingers up straight)

TEN LITTLE CLOWNS

(Also, a song)

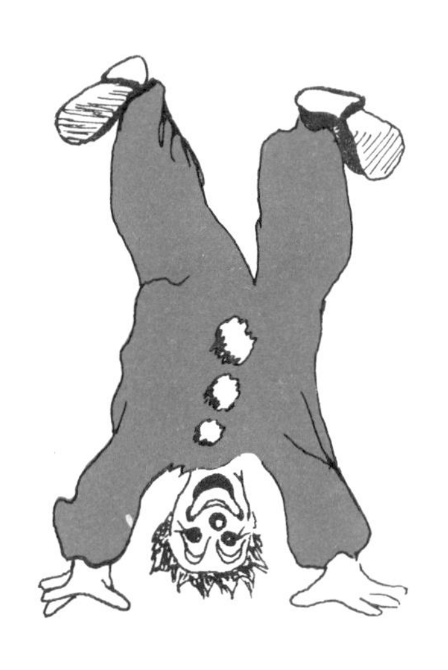

One little, two little, three little clowns,
(show a finger at each count)

Four little, five little, six little clowns,

Seven little, eight little, nine little clowns,

Ten little funny clowns.
(all fingers extended)

Ten little, nine little, eight little clowns,
(a finger comes down with each count starting with nine)

Seven little, six little, five little clowns,

Four little, three little, two little clowns,

One little funny clown.
(both hands in first position)

THIS OLD MAN

This old man, he played one,
(hold up one finger)

He played knick-knack on his thumb.
(tap thumbs together)

Knick-knack, paddy-whack, give a dog a bone,
(tap knees, clap hands, extend one hand)

This old man came rolling home.
(roll hands)

This old man, he played two,
(hold up two fingers)

He played knick-knack on his shoe.
(tap shoe)

Knick-knack, paddy-whack, give a dog a bone,
(tap knees, clap hands, extend one hand)

This old man came rolling home.
(roll hands)

This old man, he played three,
(hold up three fingers)

He played knick-knack on his knee.
(tap knee)

Knick-knack, paddy-whack, give a dog a bone,
(tap knees, clap hands, extend one hand)

This old man came rolling home.
(roll hands)

This old man, he played four,
(hold up four fingers)

He played knick-knack on the floor.
(tap floor)

Knick-knack, paddy-whack, give a dog a bone,
(tap knees, clap hands, extend one hand)

This old man came rolling home.
(roll hands)

This old man, he played five,
(hold up five fingers)

He played knick-knack on his drive.
(tap floor)

Knick-knack, paddy-whack, give a dog a bone,
(tap knees, clap hands, extend one hand)

This old man came rolling home.
(roll hands)

This old man, he played six,
(hold up six fingers)

He played knick-knack on his sticks.
(tap index fingers)

Knick-knack, paddy-whack, give a dog a bone,
(tap knees, clap hands, extend one hand)

This old man came rolling home.
(roll hands)

This old man, he played seven,
(hold up seven fingers)

He played knick-knack along to Devon.
(point outward)

Knick-knack, paddy-whack, give a dog a bone,
(tap knees, clap hands, extend one hand)

This old man came rolling home.
(roll hands)

This old man, he played eight,
(hold up eight fingers)

He played knick-knack on his plate.
(tap table)

Knick-knack, paddy-whack, give a dog a bone,
(tap knees, clap hands, extend one hand)

This old man came rolling home.
(roll hands)

This old man, he played nine,
(hold up nine fingers)

He played knick-knack on his spine.
(tap spine)

Knick-knack, paddy-whack, give a dog a bone,
(tap knees, clap hands, extend one hand)

This old man came rolling home.
(roll hands)

This old man, he played ten,
(hold up ten fingers)

He played knick-knack now and then.
(clap hands)

Knick-knack, paddy-whack, give a dog a bone,
(tap knees, clap hands, extend one hand)

This old man came rolling home.
(roll hands)

RAILROAD TRAIN

One is the engine, shiny and fine;
(hold up one finger)

It pulls the coaches all in a line.

Two is the baggage car, big and strong;
(hold up two fingers)

It carries suitcases and trunks along.

Three is the express car with double locks;
(hold up three fingers)

Send what you wish in a package or box.

Four is the mail car with much to do;
(hold up four fingers)

It carries letters to me and to you.

Five, six, and seven go all the way;
(hold up five, six, and seven fingers)

They carry people, both night and day.

Eight is the pullman, with berths one and two;
(hold up eight fingers)

Where we can sleep the whole night through.

Nine is the dining car, with tables so neat;
(hold up nine fingers)

It's where I go when I want to eat.

Ten is the observation car that gives a wide view;
(hold up ten fingers)

It lets you see the countryside as you pass through.

This is the train, all ready to go

Through sunshine, wind, rain, and snow.

TWO MOTHER PIGS

Two mother pigs lived in a pen,
(show thumbs)

Each had four babies and that made ten.
(show fingers and thumbs)

These four babies were black as night,
(hold one hand up, thumb in palm)

These four babies were black and white.
(hold other hand up, thumb in palm)

But all eight babies loved to play,

And they rolled and rolled in the pen all day.
(roll hands over each other)

At night, with their mothers, they curled up in a heap
(make fists, palms up)

And squealed and squealed till they went to sleep.

CHAPTER III

ME, MYSELF AND I

MR. NOBODY

I know a funny little man,
As quiet as a mouse,
Who does the mischief that is done
In everybody's house!
There's no one ever sees his face,
And yet we all agree
That very plate we break was cracked
By Mr. Nobody.

'Tis he who always tears out books,
Who leaves the door ajar,
He pulls the buttons from our shirts,
And scatters toys afar.
The papers always are mislaid,
Who had them last but he?
There's no one tosses them about
But Mr. Nobody.

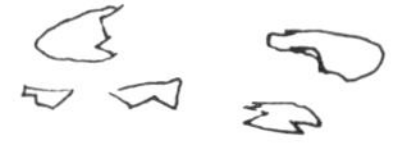

EYE WINKER

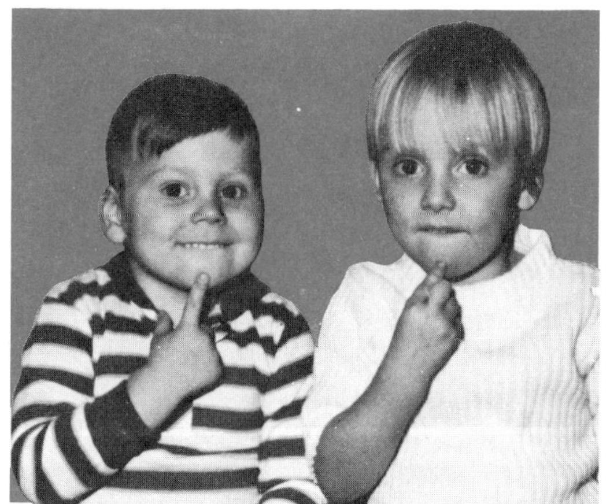

Little eye winker,
(point to eyes)

Little nose smeller,
(point to nose)

Little mouth eater,
(point to mouth)

Little chin chopper,
(tap chin)

Chin, chin, chin.

WHERE IS THUMBKIN?

(Sung to "Frere Jacques")

Where is Thumbkin? Where is Thumbkin?
(put hands behind back)

Here I am,
(show one thumb)

Here I am.
(show other thumb)

How are you this morning?
(bend one thumb)

Very well, I thank you.
(bend other thumb)

Run and play, run and play.
(put thumbs behind back)

LOOK AT ME

Look at the things I can do.

I can bend over and see my shoe,
(bend at waist and look at shoe)

I can stretch my arms up so high,
(raise arms above head)

I can look up and see the sky.
(look up)

FEE, FIE, FOE, FUM

Fee,

Fie,

Foe,

Fum.
(point to each finger for "fee", etc.)

See my fingers,
(wiggle fingers)

See my thumb.
(raise thumb)

Finger's gone,
(curl fingers into palm)

So is thumb.
(close thumbs under fingers, making fist)

MY HAT

My hat, it has three corners,
(join thumbs and index fingers and place on top of head)

Three corners has my hat.
(raise three fingers)

If it did not have three corners,
(keep three fingers up and shake head)

It would not be my hat.
(join thumbs and index fingers and place on top of head)

ME

This is my nose,
(point to body parts as indicated)

These are my ears,

These are my eyes

That make the tears.

This is my mouth,

It smiles when I'm gay.

I think I'll always keep

Just that way!
(smile big)

HOW BABY GROWS

Five fingers on this hand,
(hold up one hand)

Five fingers on that,
(hold up other hand)

A dear little nose,
(point to nose)

A mouth like a rose,
(point to mouth)

Two cheeks so tiny and fat,
(point to cheeks)

Two eyes — two ears,
(point to eyes and ears)

And ten little toes,
(point to toes)

That's the way baby grows.

CLAP YOUR HANDS

Clap your hands, clap your hands,
(action is indicated by rhyme)

Clap them just like me.

Touch your shoulders, touch your shoulders,

Touch them just like me.

Tap your knees, tap your knees,

Tap them just like me.

Shake your head, shake your head,

Shake it just like me.

Clap your hands, clap your hands,

Now let them quiet be.
(fold hands in lap)

GUESS WHAT I SEE

If I look in the mirror,
(forefingers and thumbs circled over eyes)

Guess what I see.

Someone who looks,

Just like me!
(point to self)

And if you stand beside me,

It is also true,

I can see someone who looks
(forefingers and thumbs circling eyes)

Just like you.
(point to another)

PEASE PORRIDGE HOT

(two children facing each other)

Pease[1] porridge[2] hot,[3]
Pease[1] porridge[2] cold,[3]
Pease[1] porridge[2] in the[4] pot[2]
Nine[5] days[2] old.[3]

Some[1] like it[2] hot[3],
Some[1] like it[2] cold,[3]
Some[1] like it[2] in the[4] pot[2]
Nine[5] days[2] old.[3]

[1]*Clap hands on lap.*
[2]*Clap hands together.*
[3]*Clap with partner's hands.*
[4]*Clap right hand's together.*
[5]*Clap left hand's together.*

HELPFULNESS

This little boy does nothing but play,
(hold up thumb)

This little child wants his way,
(Put up index finger)

This is a boy so strong and tall,
(put up middle finger)

This child will not help at all.
(put up ring finger)

Here's one who's kind and true,
(put up little finger)

Always helping, just like you.
(point to child)

FINGERS

Kind little finger people,
(hold up hands, look at fingers)

Who'll put the toys away?

"I will, I will, I will, I will,
(wiggle fingers)

I will," the fingers say.
(fingers run away)

HANDS ON SHOULDERS

Hands on shoulders, hands on knees,
(follow action as rhyme indicates)

Hands behind you, if you please.

Touch your shoulders, now your nose,

Now your hair and now your toes.

Hands up high in the air,

Down at your sides and touch your chair.

Hands up high as before,

Now clap your hands,

One, two, three, four.

DO YOUR EARS HANG LOW?

(Also, a song)

Do your ears hang low?
(hands extending downward by ears)

Do they wobble to and fro?
(hands wobble)

Can you tie them in a knot?
(pretend to tie knot)

Can you tie them in a bow?
(pretend to tie bow)

Can you toss them over your shoulder
(make appropriate motion)

Like a continental soldier?

Do your ears hang low?
(hands extending downward by ears)

Do your ears hang high?
(put hands by ears, fingers upward)

Do they reach up to the sky?
(hands move upward until arms extended)

Are they curly when they're wet?

Are they shaggy when they're dry?

Can you toss them over your shoulder
(make tossing motion over shoulder)

Like a continental soldier.

Do your ears hang high?
(hands by ears, fingers upward)

RIGHT HAND, LEFT HAND

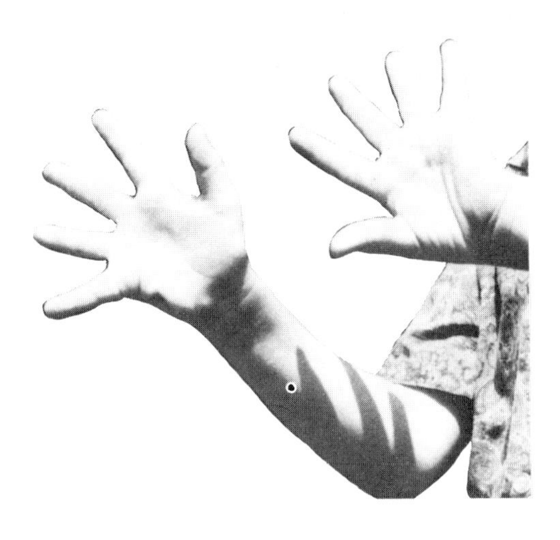

This is my right hand,
(follow action as rhyme indicates)

I'll raise it up high.

This is my left hand,

I'll touch the sky.

Right hand, left hand,

Roll them around.

Left hand, right hand,

Pound, pound, pound.
(pound fist in other palm)

FOUR YEARS OLD

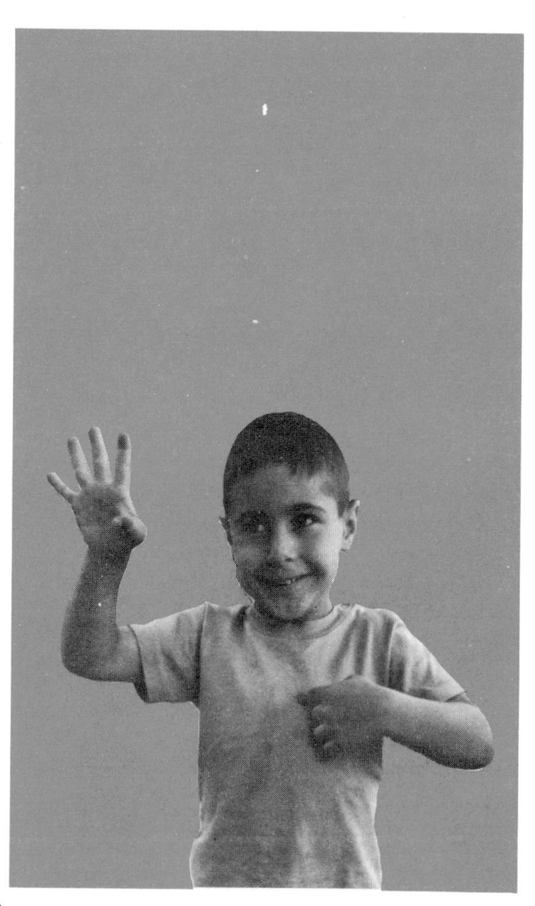

Please, everyone, come with me
(beckon with arm motion)

Today's my birthday, don't you see.

Yesterday I was only three,
(hold up three fingers)

But I'm four today, you see.
(four fingers up, point to self with other index finger)

Today I'm four, not two or one,
(hold up number of fingers indicated)

We'll have a party and lots of fun.

I'll be four one year and then
(four fingers up)

I'll never, ever be four again.
(fingers down, shake head no)

SHIVER AND QUIVER

When it's cold I shiver and quiver,
(clasp arms and shiver)

B-r-r-r, b-r-r-r, b-r-r-r.

When it's cold I quiver and shiver,
(clasp arms and shiver)

B-r-r-r, b-r-r-r, b-r-r-r.

When my hands feel like ice,

I rub them hard once or twice.
(rub hands vigorously)

B-r-r-r, b-r-r-r, b-r-r-r.

If I'm cold from head to toe,
(point to head and feet)

Into my house I must go.

SIMON SAYS

Simon says, "Thumbs up!"
(children put thumbs up)

Simon says, "Thumbs down!"
(put thumbs down)

Simon says, "Thumbs up!"
(put thumbs up)

"Thumbs down!"
(child is caught *and becomes "It" if he puts thumbs down)*

(Do only the things that Simon says. You are caught *if you do something that Simon doesn't say.)*

(Try varying this with other directions, such as clapping—high, low, front, back, etc.)

NOT ALWAYS

Finger plays are great fun,
But not *always* for everyone.

CHAPTER IV ANIMALS

If I had a hundred dollars to spend,

Or maybe a little more,

I'd hurry as fast as my legs would go

Straight to the animal store.

TROT–TROT–TROT

Trot, trot, trot, trot, trot, trot, trot,
(make fingers trot on arm)

Trot my little pony — trot,

Trot, trot, trot, trot, trot, trot, trot,
(make fingers trot on arm)

Trot my little pony, trot.

Lift your little legs so high,
(lift fingers high)

Toss your head as you walk by,
(toss head)

Trot, trot, trot, trot, trot, trot, trot,
(make fingers trot on arm)

Stop my little pony, stop.
(stop fingers)

(Vary this by using paper cup on table to make sound of hoof beats.)

TWO LITTLE BLACKBIRDS

Two little blackbirds,
(close fists, extend index finger)

Sitting on a hill.

One named Jack,
(talk to one index finger)

And the other named Jill.
(talk to other index finger)

Fly away Jack,
(toss index fingers over shoulders separately)

Fly away Jill.

Come back Jack,
(bring back hands separately with index fingers extended)

Come back Jill.

LITTLE MISS MUFFET

Little Miss Muffet,
(right hand fist, thumb extended; make fist of left hand)

Sat on a tuffet,
(place right fist on left fist)

Eating her curds and whey.
(eating motion with left hand)

Along came a spider,
(use left hand in walking motion)

And sat down beside her,
(walk left hand beside right fist)

And frightened Miss Muffet away.
(throw hand out in sudden motion)

EENSY, WEENSY SPIDER

Eensy, weensy spider
(let opposite thumbs and index fingers climb up each other)

Climbed up the water spout.

Down came the rain,
(let hands sweep down and arms open wide)

And washed the spider out.

Out came the sun,
(form circle over head with arms)

And dried up all the rain.

So the eensy, weensy spider,

Climbed up the spout again.
(let opposite thumbs and fingers climb up each other again)

KITTY

This is kitty sleek and gray,
(hold up thumb)

With her kittens four.
(hold up four fingers of other hand)

She went to sleep one summer day
(lay head on folded hands as if asleep)

By the kitchen door.

HICKORY, DICKORY, DOCK

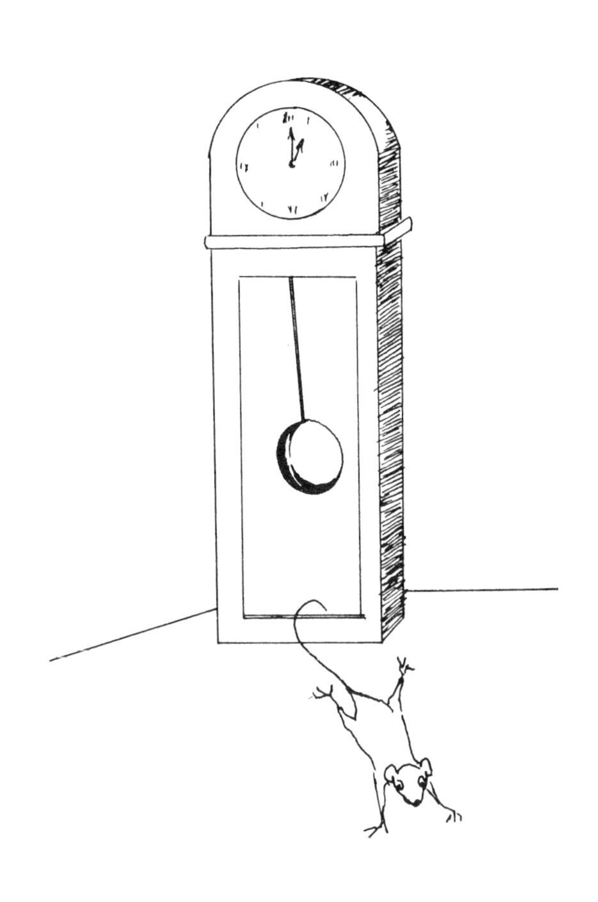

Hickory, dickory, dock,
(bend arm at elbow; hold up, palm open)

The mouse ran up the clock.
(run fingers of other hand up arm)

The clock struck one,
(hold up index finger of hand representing clock or clap hands once)

The mouse ran down.
(run fingers down arm)

Hickory, dickory, dock.

THE CAT AND HER KITTENS

"Kitty, kitty, kitty, kitty,
(make fist, raise one finger at a time of one hand)

All my little ones so pretty,
(make fist of other hand, thumb extended, raise thumb, bend to make as if speaking)

Let me hear how you can mew."
(continue bending thumb for words)

"Mew, mew, mew, mew."
(said by children, four fingers bend)

"Kitty, kitty, kitty, kitty,
(other hand, raise one finger at a time)

All my little ones so pretty,
(raise thumbs and bend to match words)

Curl up close now, just like that.
(curl fingers into palm, thumbs up)

Go to sleep," says mother cat.
(children close eyes, thumbs bend as if speaking, then fold thumbs over fingers)

"Sleep till someone calls out 'SCAT'."
(spread arms in startled motion)

THREE LITTLE MONKEYS

Three little monkeys
(hold up three fingers)

Jumping on the bed.
(bounce fingers)

One fell off and bumped his head.
(point to head)

Took him to the doctor; the doctor said,
(rock arms as if cradle)

That's what you get
(shake finger reprovingly)

For jumping on the bed."

MY TURTLE

This is my turtle,
(make fist, extend thumb)

He lives in a shell.
(hide thumb in fist)

He likes his home very well.

He pokes his head out when he wants to eat,
(extend thumb)

And pulls it back in when he wants to sleep.
(hide thumb in fist)

KITTEN IS HIDING

A kitten is hiding under a chair,
(hide one thumb in other hand)

I looked and looked for her everywhere.
(peer about hand on forehead)

Under the table and under the bed,
(pretend to look)

I looked in the corner and then I said,

"Come kitty, come kitty, I have milk for you."
(cup hands to make dish and extend)

Kitty came running and calling, "Mew, mew."
(run fingers up arm)

THE BUNNY

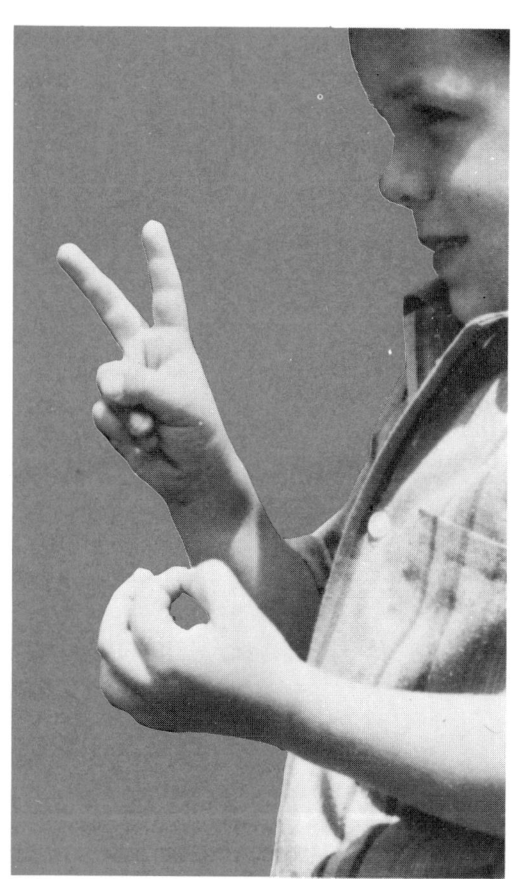

This is the bunny with ears so funny,
(hold up two fingers)

And this is his hole in the ground.
(make circle with thumb and finger of other hand)

When a noise he hears, he pricks up his ears;
(straighten fingers up)

Then runs to his hole in the ground.
(put pointed fingers in "hole")

LITTLE MICE

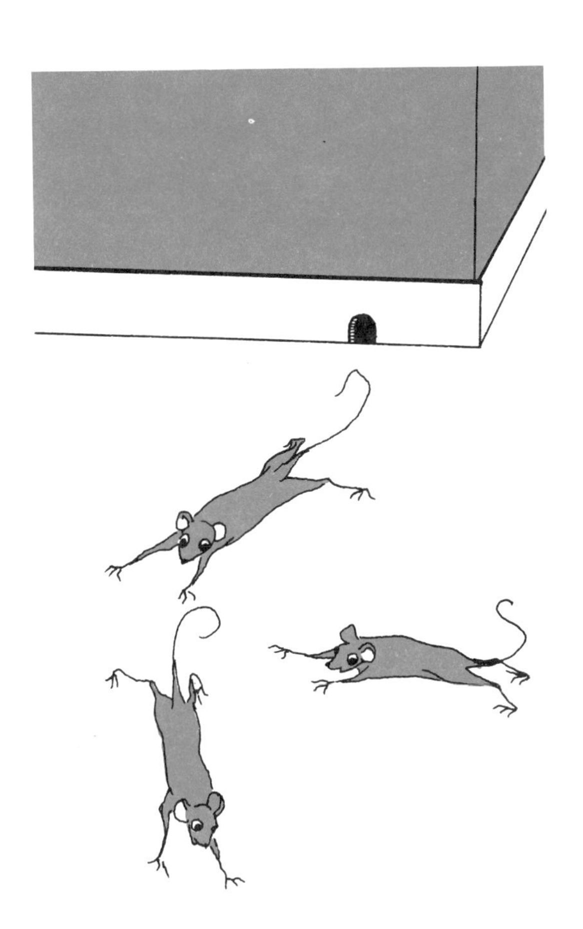

The little mice are creeping, creeping, creeping;
    (creep fingers along arm)

The little mice are creeping through the house.

The little mice are sleeping, sleeping, sleeping;
    (fold hands under cheek and close eyes)

The little mice are sleeping in the house.

The old gray cat comes creeping, creeping, creeping;
    (creep fingers along other arm)

The old gray cat comes creeping through the house.

The little mice all scamper, scamper, scamper;
    (fingers run away)

The little mice all scamper through the house.

LITTLE DUCKS

Some little ducks that I once knew,
(extend index finger)

Fat ducks, skinny ducks, other ones too,
(shake index finger to emphasize)

But the one little duck with feathers on his back,
(emphasize one with index finger)

He led the others with a quack, quack, quack,
(bend arms at elbows, tuck hands in armpits, flap arms up and down)

Quack, quack, quack.
(continue above motion)

Down to the river they would go,
(put hands together and wiggle in front of body)

Wobble, wobble, wobble, wobble to and fro.

But the one little duck with the feathers on his back,
(emphasize one)

He led the others with a quack, quack, quack,
(bend arms at elbows, tuck hands in armpits, flap arms up and down)

He led the others with a quack, quack, quack,

Quack, quack, quack.

SING A SONG OF SIXPENCE

Sing a song of sixpence, a pocket full of rye,

Four and twenty blackbirds baked in a pie.
(make a circle with arms)

When the pie was opened,
(arms extended, palms up)

The birds began to sing.
(flutter fingers)

Wasn't that a dainty dish to set before a king?

The king was in his counting house,
(cup one hand loosely)

Counting out his money.
(pick up "money" with other)

The queen was in the parlor,

Eating bread and honey.
(make eating motions)

The maid was in the garden,

Hanging out the clothes.
(hands extended up)

When down came a blackbird,
(flutter one hand down)

And nipped off her nose!
(nip nose)

LITTLE COTTAGE IN THE WOOD

Little cottage in the wood,
(hands meet at fingertips, making house)

Little man by the window stood.
(fingers encircle eyes, looking)

Saw a rabbit running by,
(fingers of one hand move and arms extends forward)

Frightened as could be,
(wrap arms around self)

"Help me! Help me!", the rabbit said,
(both hands fly up and down)

"Before those hunters shoot me dead."
(finger pointed as gun)

"Come little rabbit, come with me,
(hand beckons)

Happy we will be."
(one hand strokes other closed fist)

MAGIC MIRROR

I have a magic mirror in my mind,

Where there are animals of every kind.

It opens the door and lets me see

All the things I'd like to be.

If I had a nose as long as a hose,
(both fists on nose, extend one fist outward)

And a tail you can hardly see,
(measure with index finger and thumb)

Then a gigantic elephant I would be!
(stretch arms as far as possible)

A hundred teeth lined up in a smile,
(big smile)

Will make me a ferocious crocodile.
(big growl — g-r-r-r-r-r)

When I put antlers right up here,
(fingers spread, thumbs on head)

I can be a graceful deer.

Animals of every kind

Are in this magic mirror of my mind.

Now you can make up verses too,

How about a giraffe or a kangaroo?

Perhaps a bird up in a tree,

Or a little hive for a honeybee?

Take your turn. Oh, give it a try!

It's time for me to say goodbye.

CHAPTER V PEOPLE I KNOW

HAPPY PEOPLE

Some people are tall and thin,

Some people are big and wide,

But it really doesn't matter,

If they're happy inside.

ROCK-A-BYE BABY

Rock-a-bye baby on a tree top,
    (fold arms)

When the wind blows, the cradle will rock;
    (rock arms)

When the bow breaks, the cradle will fall.

Down will come rock-a-bye baby and all.
    (make falling motion)

PEEK-A-BOO

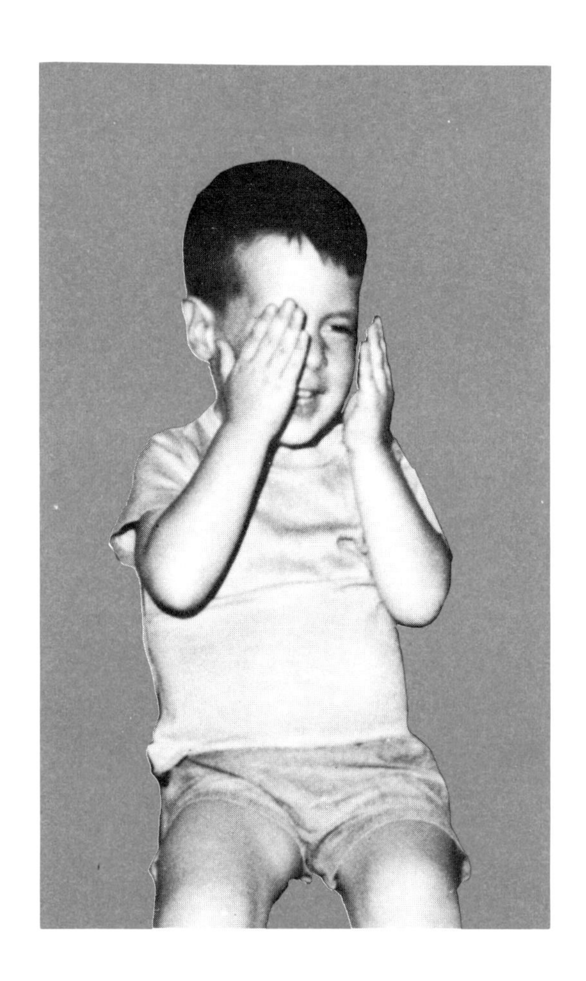

Here is the way that baby

Plays at peek-a-boo.
(play peek-a-boo with fingers)

Here is baby's cradle,
(fold arms to make cradle)

Rock-a-baby-bye.
(rock folded arms)

JACK BE NIMBLE

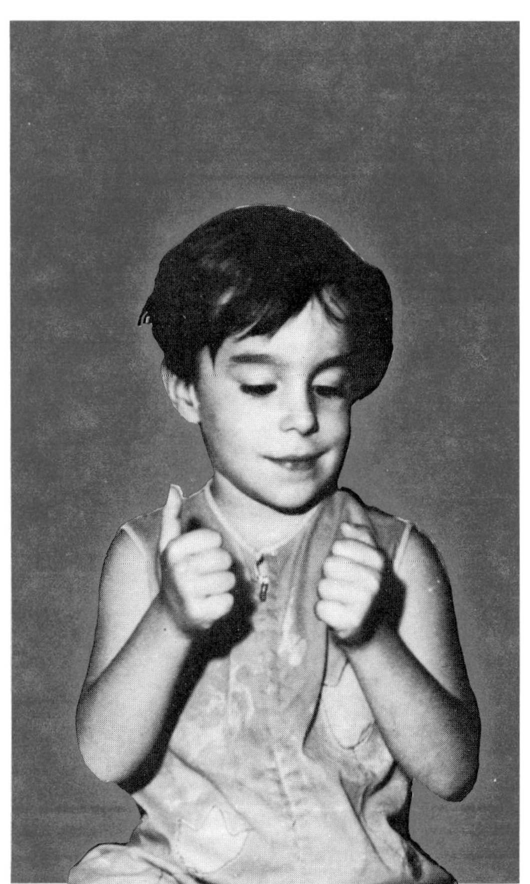

Jack be nimble,
(hold closed fist with thumb standing)

Jack be quick,
(hold up other fist)

Jack jumped over the candlestick.
(first hand hops over other fist)

PAT-A-CAKE

Pat-a-cake, pat-a-cake, baker's man,
(clap hands in rhythm)

Bake me a cake as fast as you can.
(pat palm of one hand with fingers of other)

Pat it and prick it and mark it with a "T",
(pat hands firmly)

And put it in the oven for baby and me.
(move hands forward as if putting in oven)

HERE'S A BALL FOR BABY

Here is a ball for baby,
(make ball with both hands)

Big and soft and round.

Here is baby's hammer,
(make hammer with fist, hammer on other fist)

Oh, how he can pound!

Here is baby's music,
(hold hands facing each other)

Clapping, clapping, so.
(clap)

THE FAMILY

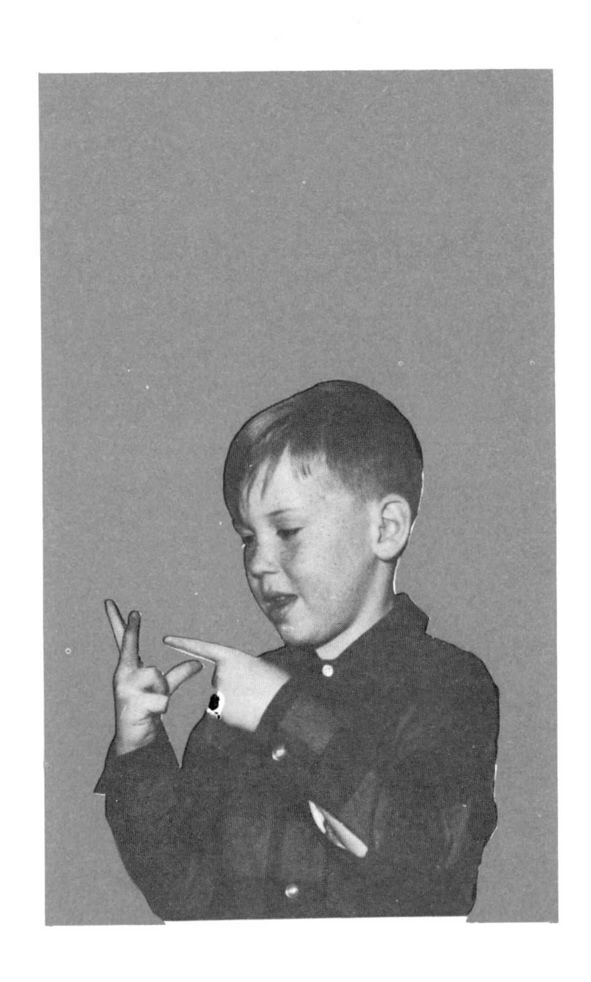

This is my father,
(point to thumb)

This is my mother,
(point to index finger)

This is my brother tall.
(point to middle finger)

This is my sister,
(point to ring finger)

This is the baby,
(point to little finger)

Oh, how we love them all.
(clap hands)

COBBLER, COBBLER

Cobbler, cobbler, mend my shoe,
(hold one foot on other knee)

Have it done by half past two.
(hammer shoe with fist)

Stitch it up and stitch it down,
(make sewing motions on shoe)

Now nail the heel all around.
(make hammering motions around shoe heel)

MY MOTHER AND YOUR MOTHER

My mother and your mother
(close fists with thumbs up)

Went over the way.
(make fists walk forward)

Said my mother to your mother,
(bow thumbs to each other)

"Let's go shopping today."

"O.K.!"
(fists rush behind back)

MAN IN THE BOX

Down in a box
(close fist with thumb tucked in, cover with flat palm of other hand)

Is a little tiny man.

He waits and waits

Just as quiet as he can,

Until I open the lid,
(raise palm covering fist)

Pop!
(thumb pops out)

LITTLE BOY BLUE

Little Boy Blue

Come blow your horn,
(pretend to blow horn)

The sheep are in the meadow,
(right arm gestures toward right)

The cows are in the corn.
(left arm gestures toward left)

Where's the little boy,

That looks after the sheep?
(hand over eyes, peer about)

He is under the hay stack,

Fast asleep.
(hands under cheek, eyes closed)

Will you wake him?

No, not I,
(shake head, "no")

For if I do he'll surely cry.
(pretend to cry, fingers tracing tears down cheek)

JACK AND JILL

Jack and Jill went up the hill,
(extend hands out flat, palms facing down; climb them upwards)

To fetch a pail of water.

Jack fell down and broke his crown,
(let one hand fall quickly into lap)

And Jill came tumbling after.
(let other hand follow jerkily)

Up Jack got and said to Jill,
(raise one hand and then the other)

As in his arms he caught her,
(cross arms and hug shoulders)

"If you're not hurt, brush off the dirt,
(brush off clothes)

And then we'll fetch the water."

S-l-o-w-l-y, s-l-o-w-l-y, up the hill,
(climb hands up slowly)

This time they spilled no water.

They took it home to mother dear,
(close fist and seem to carry bucket)

Who kissed her son and daughter.
(kissing sound)

HERE IS THE CHURCH

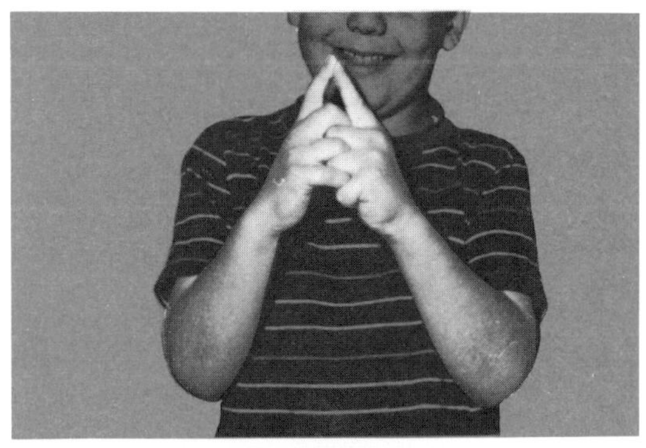

Here is the church,
(put backs of hands together, palms down, fingers interlaced)

Here is the steeple.
(extend index fingers to make a point)

Open the door,
(turn hands around, fingers still clasped, pointing upward)

And see all the people.
(wiggle fingers)

OUR HOUSE

These are mother's knives and forks,
(put backs of hands together, fingers interlaced and pointing upward)

This is father's table.
(turn hands over, fingers interlaced, palms and fingers facing down)

This is sister's looking glass,
(palms, fingers still interlaced, in front of face)

And this is baby's cradle.
(point index and little fingers to make cradle, palms facing down, rock hands sideways)

HERE I AM

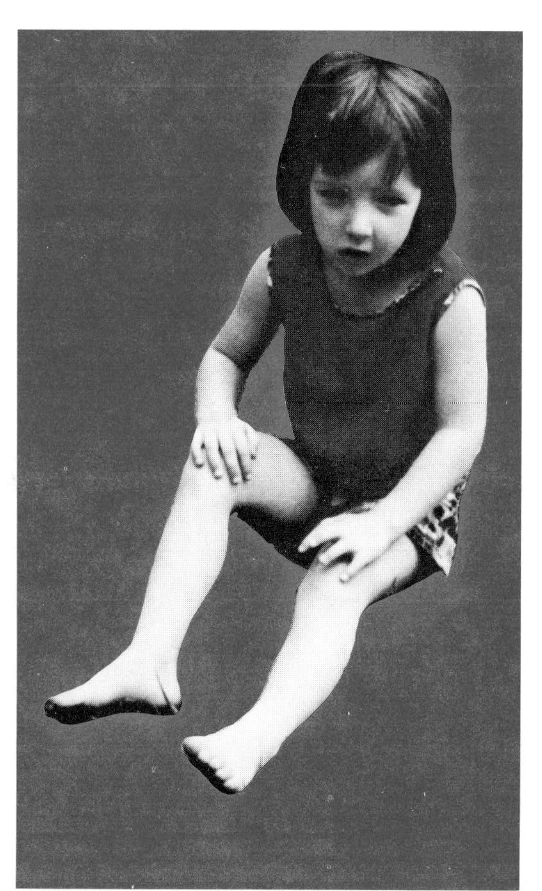

Here I am,
(close fist on one hand, thumb up)

Here I am,

Little jumping Joan.
("jump" thumb around)

When nobody's with me,

I'm always alone.

GOOD MORNING, MOTHER

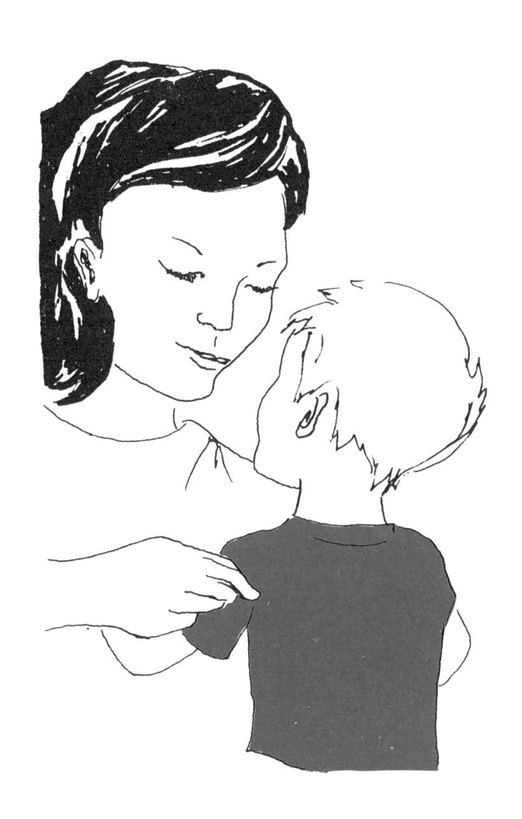

Good morning, mother, how do you do.
(hold up one thumb)

Good morning, daddy, I'm glad to see you.
(hold up other thumb)

Good, little mother, I have a kiss for you.
(kiss thumb)

Good, dear daddy, a kiss for you too!
(kiss other thumb)

A VISITOR

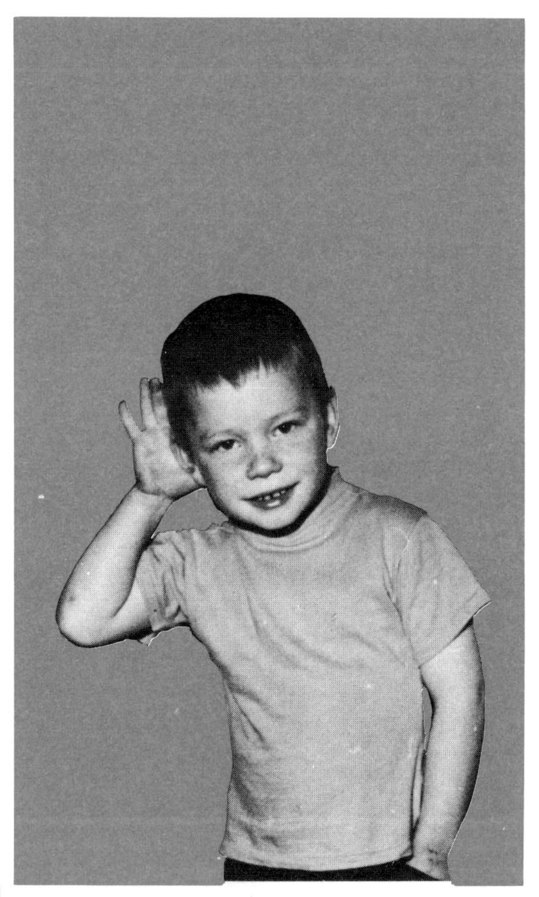

I heard a little tiny noise,
(listen, hand cupped over ear)

Behind the cupboard door;

And something soft and small and quick,

Flashed right across the floor.
(make quick motion with hand)

The day had very nearly gone,

And I could hardly see,
(hand above eyes, peering)

I do so wish that it would come again

To visit me.
(point to self)

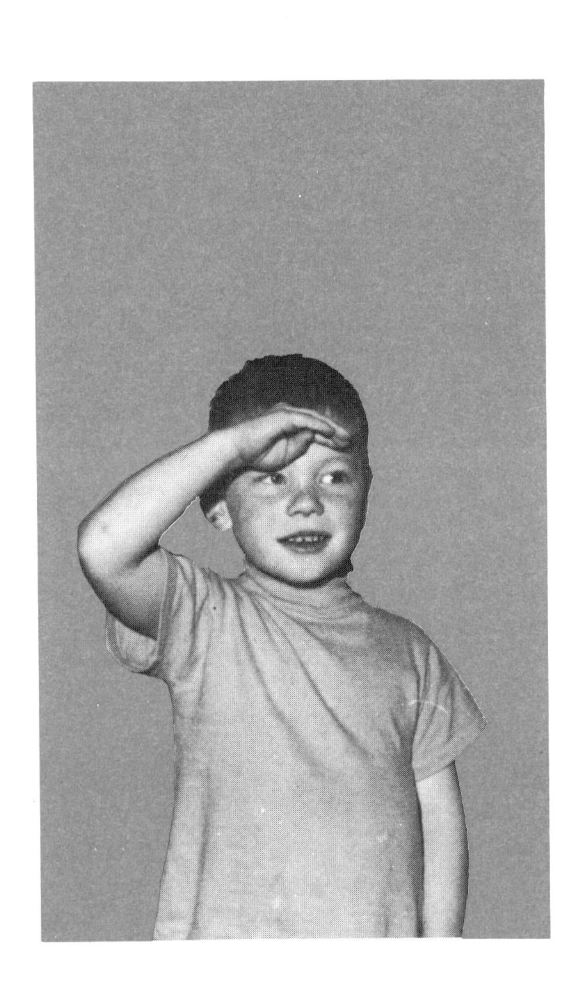

The whole day long I've looked and looked

And looked about the house.
(look all around)

I think it was a fairy,
(point to self)

Mother thinks it was a mouse.
(gesture outward with hand)

CRADLE

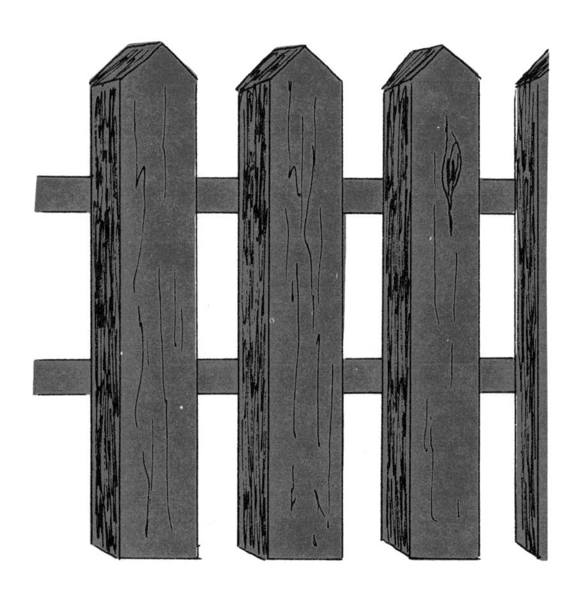

This is the fence around the yard,
(arms outstretched, hands together)

This is a house for mother.
(hands form roof shape)

This is the church for all of us,
(fingers clasped inside hand, point index fingers as steeple)

And this is the cradle for brother.
(point little fingers, also rock)

THE STILT MAN

There was a great big stilt man,
(hold loose fists forward with index fingers extended, one fist slightly above the other)

Who was tall, tall, tall.
(move left fist upward)

There was a little midget,

Who was small, small, small.
(move right fist downward)

And the midget, who was small,
(wiggle lower finger)

Would try and try and try,
(move lower fist up a bit)

To reach up to the stilt man,
(wiggle left finger)

Who was tall, tall, tall.
(move left fist up further)

THE LITTLE ELF

I met a little elf-man once,
(show small size with hands)

Down where the lilies blow.

I asked him why he was so small,

And why he didn't grow.

He slightly frowned and with his eye,

He looked me through and through.

"I'm quite as big for me," said he,
(point to self)

"As you are big for you."
(point to other person)

KING OF FRANCE

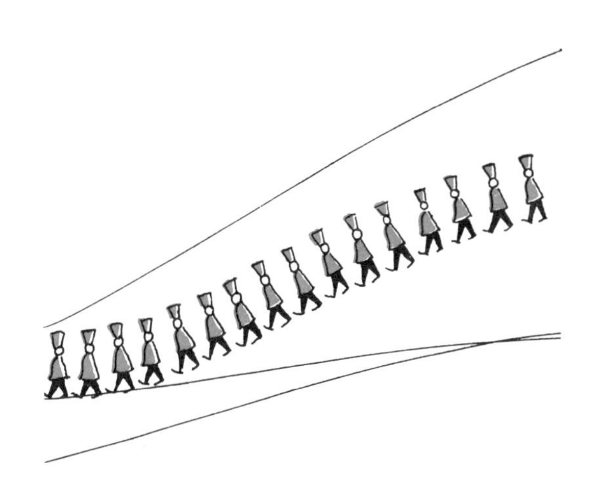

The famous King of France,

He led ten thousand men.
(palms forward, all fingers extended)

He marched them way, way up the hill,
(palms down, march hands up in air, one over the other)

And marched them down again.
(march hands down)

And when they were up,
(march hands up)

They were up, up, up.

And when they were down,
(march hands down)

They were down, down, down.

But when they were halfway up,
(hold hands halfway up)

They were also halfway down.

SECRETS

Shh, shh, shh, shh, shh,
(finger on lips)

We have a secret,

Just we three,
(hold up three fingers)

The robin and I and the sweet cherry tree.
(point to three fingers, one at a time)

Shh, shh, shh, shh, shh,

Of course the robin

Knows it best.

He built the ________.
(clap hand over mouth when omitting word)

I can't tell the rest,
(shake head "no")

And put three little somethings in it.
(raise three fingers)

I'm afraid I shall tell it every minute.

Shh, shh, shh, shh, shh.
(fingers on lips)

TEN LITTLE FIREMEN

Ten little firemen,

Sleeping in a row.
(extend both hands, palms down, fingers straight and close together to represent sleeping men)

Ding, dong goes the bell,
(pull bell cord with one hand)

And down the pole they go.
(close both fist, put one on top of other, slide them down pole)

Off on the engine, oh, oh, oh,
(steer engine with hands)

Using the big hose, so, so, so.
(make nozzle with fist)

When all the fire's out, home so-o slow,
(steer engine with hands)

Back to bed, all in a row.
(extend both hands, fingers close together and straight, palms down)

CHAPTER VI THE WORLD AROUND US

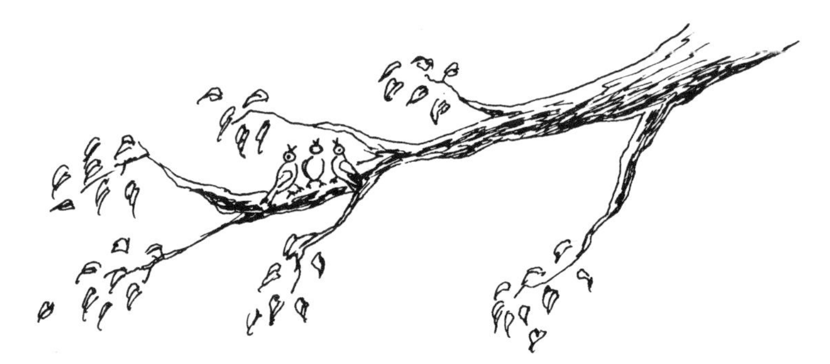

THE WORLD'S MUSIC

The world's a very happy place,

Where every child should dance and sing,

And always have a smiling face,

And never sulk for anything.

Gabriel Setoun

ROW, ROW, ROW YOUR BOAT

Row, row, row your boat

(hold arms high in front of chest with elbows extending out and fisted hands meeting, reach forward and pull back as if rowing)

Gently down the stream.

Merrily, merrily, merrily, merrily,

Life is but a dream.

RAINY DAY

Pitter pat, pitter pat,
    (raise hands high, flutter fingers down)

It's a rainy day.

I'll dress up, snug and warm,
    (pretend to put on clothes)

And go outside to play.

THE DOOR

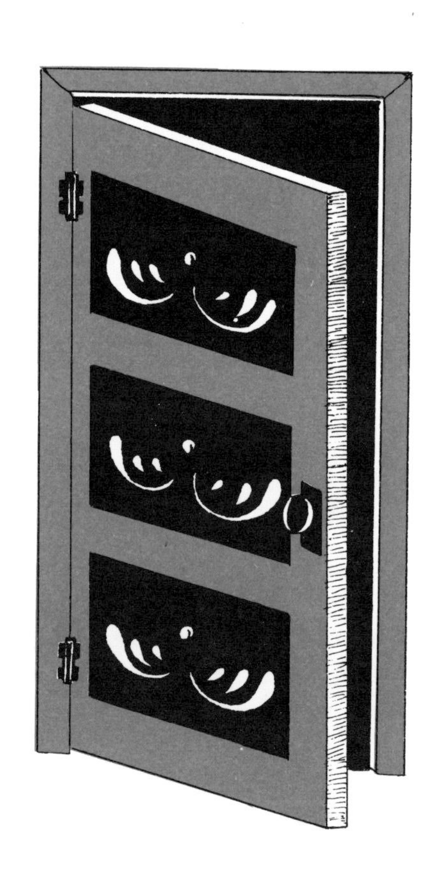

Tap at the door,
(tap on forehead)

Peep in,
(form circles with fingers and look through)

Turn the knob,
(make turning motion with hand)

Walk in,
(walk fingers along other hand)

And — shut the door!!
(clap)

SAILBOATS

I like to feel the soft wind blow,
(blow through lips)

And see how it makes the sailboats go.
(move hand in imitation of boat moving over the waves)

And watch the birds against the sky,
(hand over eyes, peer upward)

Both birds and sailboats seem to fly!
(arms extended, make flying motion)

THE TRAIN

The great big train goes down the track,
(fingers creep up arm)

It says, "Toot, toot," and then goes back.
(fingers creep down arm)

Choo-choo-choo-choo,

Choo-choo-choo-choo.

HAMMERING

Bang, bang with your hammer,
(make fist with one hand, extend thumb up)

Pound, pound, pound the nail,
(pound thumb with other fist)

Pound the nail down tight.
(pound thumb slowly with other fist)

THE FIREMAN'S HAT

Once I wore a fireman's hat,
(hands on head making hat)

And stood by an engine, just like that!
(stand straight, arms at side)

FIRE TRUCK

I'd like to be a fireman on a big red truck,

I'd drive fast to the fires and wouldn't get stuck,
(hands as though on steering wheel)

I'd wear a hat, and what do you think?
(hands on head making hat)

I'd put out the fires as quick as a wink!
(pretend holding hose and move arms at though moving hose)

S-s-s-s-s-s-s-s-s

THE AIRPLANE

The airplane has great big wings,
(arms outstretched at shoulders)

And a propeller that goes round and sings.
(circle both arms in front)

It goes up, up, up, up, up,
(move both arms up)

It goes down, down, down, down, down.
(move arms down)

HERE'S A CUP

Here's a cup, and here's a cup,
(make a circle with thumb and index finger of open hand, extend arm and repeat)

And here's a pot of tea.
(make fist with other hand and extend thumb for spout)

Pour a cup, and pour a cup,
(tip fist to pour)

And have a drink with me.
(make drinking motions)

CLOCKS

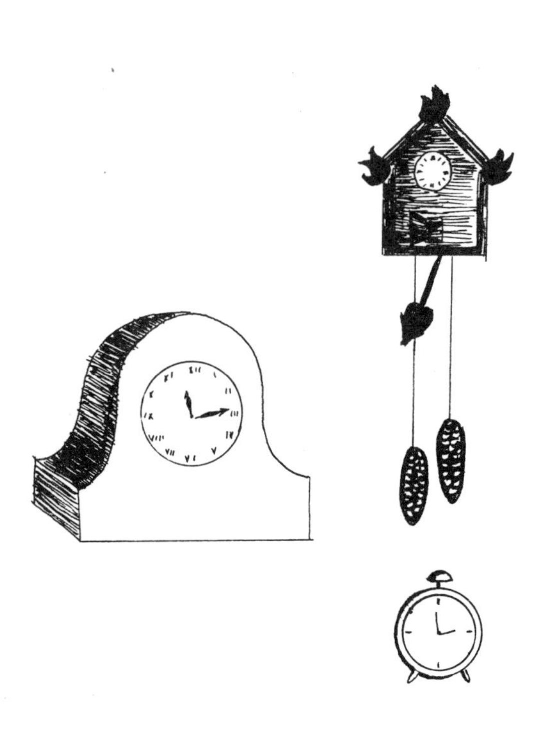

Big clocks make a sound like t-i-c-k, t-o-c-k, t-i-c-k, t-o-c-k,
(rest elbows on hips, extend forearms and index fingers up and move arms sideways slowly and rhythmically)

Small clocks make a sound like tick, tock, tick, tock,
(move arms faster for second time)

And the very tiny clocks make a sound like tick, tock, tick, tock,

Tick, tock, tick, tock, tick, tock, tick, tock, tick.

I HAVE A LITTLE WATCH

I have a little watch right here,
(make circle with thumb and index finger for watch)

Hold it way up near your ear.
(hold circle close to ear)

Hear it ticking, ticking fast?

It tells us when our playtime's past.

HERE IS THE ENGINE

Here is the engine on the track;
(hold up thumb)

Here is the coal car, just in back;
(hold up pointer finger)

Here is the boxcar to carry freight;
(hold up middle finger)

Here is the mail car, don't be late!
(hold up ring finger)

Way back here at the end of the train.
(hold up little finger)

Comes the caboose through the sun and the rain.

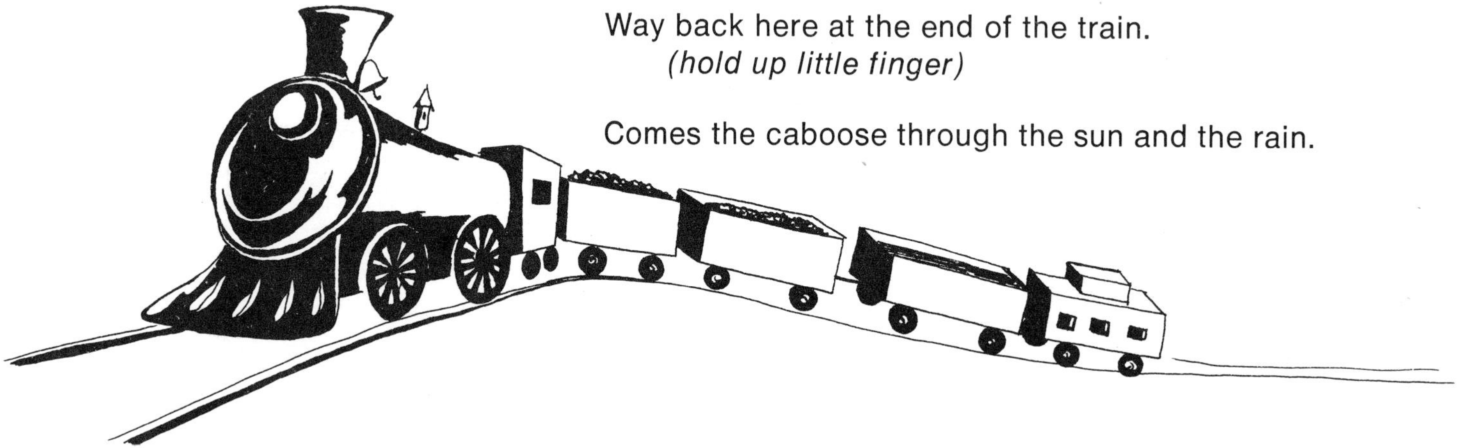

DOWN BY THE STATION

Down by the station early in the morning,
(clap hands in rhythm)

See the little engines standing in a row.
(place hand on forehead as if peering)

See the engineer pull the little handle,
(pull down handle)

Toot, toot, choo, choo, off we go.
(say "toot" in high voice, slide palms together for choo-choo)

WINDOW PANE

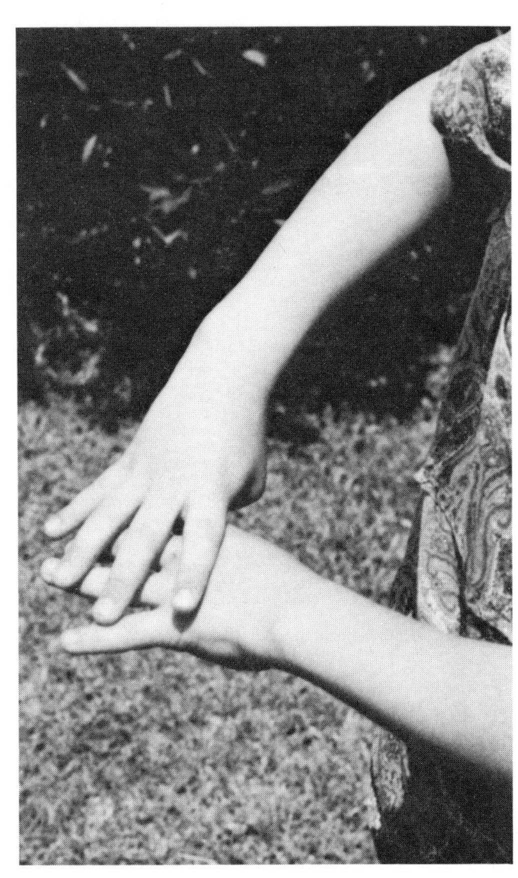

I have a checkered window pane,
(cross opened fingers)

I close the blinds at night,
(close fingers)

And in the morning, open them,
(open fingers)

Because I love the light.

CHOO-CHOO TRAIN

This is a choo-choo train,
(bend arms at elbows)

Puffing down the track.
(rotate forearms in rhythm)

Now it's going forward,
(push arms forward, continue rotating motion)

Now it's going back.
(pull arms back, continue rotating motion)

Now the bell is ringing,
(pull bell cord with closed fist)

Now the whistle blows.
(hold fist near mouth and blow, "toot, toot")

What a lot of noise it makes
(cover ears with hands)

Everywhere it goes.
(stretch out arms)

WE WASH OUR CLOTHES

(Also can be sung to "Here We Go 'Round the Mulberry Bush")

This is the way we wash our clothes,

Wash our clothes, wash our clothes.

This is the way we wash our clothes,

So early in the morning.
(hold fists close together and scrub together)

This is the way we hang our clothes,

Hang our clothes, hang our clothes.

This is the way we hang our clothes,

So early in the morning.
(raise arms as though hanging clothes)

This is the way we iron our clothes,

Iron our clothes, iron our clothes.

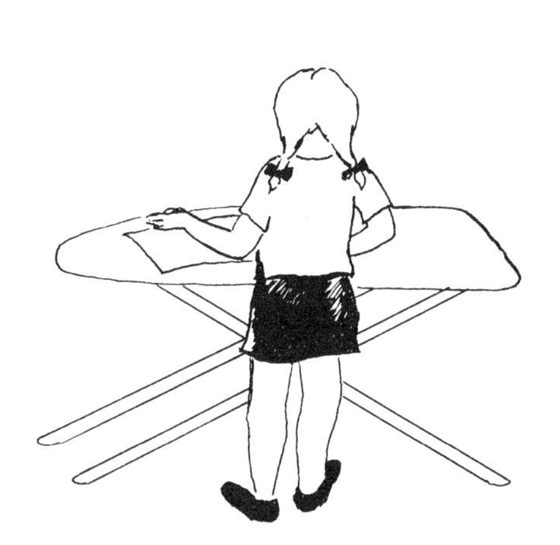

This is the way we iron our clothes,

So early in the morning.

(make a fist for iron and glide over other arm)

This is the way we mend our clothes,

Mend our clothes, mend our clothes.

This is the way we mend our clothes,

So early in the morning.

(hold one hand in front and make sewing motions on it with other hand)

This is the way we fold our clothes,

Fold our clothes, fold our clothes.

This is the way we fold our clothes,

So early in the morning.

(make appropriate folding motions)

THE WASHBOARD

Here's a little water,
(turn right wrist as if turning on faucet)

Here's a little tub,
(make circle with two arms)

Here's a little cake of soap,
(circle with two hands)

Here's the clothes we rub,

And this is the way we rub.
(motion of rubbing clothes)

Here's a line way up high,
(middle fingers only touch above head, making line)

Now the clothes can dry.

THE TEAPOT

I'm a little teapot, short and stout.

This is my handle,
(put one hand on hip)

This is my spout.
(extend opposite arm sideways, hand out)

When I get all steamed up, then I shout,

Just tip me over and pour me out.
(bend body toward extended arm)

S-S-S-S-S

I'm a clever teapot, it is true.

Here is something I can do.

I can change my handle and my spout,
(change position of hands)

Just tip me over and pour me out.
(bend body toward extended arm)

S-S-S-S-S

THE BUS

The wheels of the bus go round and round,

Round and round, round and round.
(roll hands)

The wheels of the bus go round and round,

Over the city streets.

The driver of the bus blows his horn,

Beep-beep-beep, beep-beep-beep.
(press thumb on fist)

The driver of the bus blows his horn,

Over the city streets.

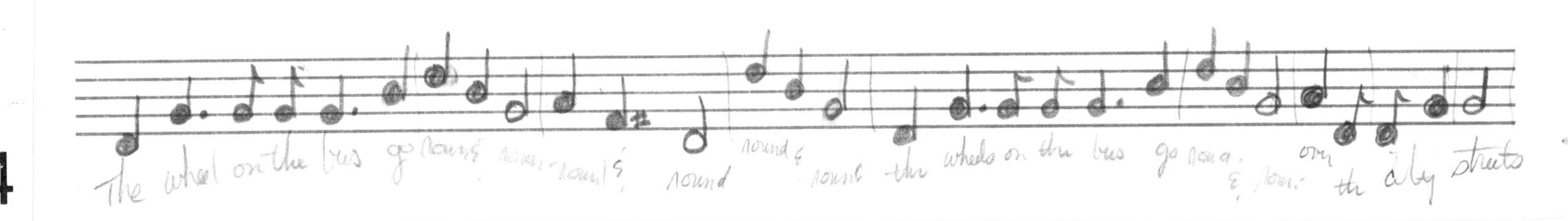

The driver of the bus says, "Pay your fare,

Pay your fare, pay your fare."

(extend hand as if receiving fare)

The driver of the bus says, "Pay your fare,"

Over the city streets.

The people on the bus go bump, bump, bump,

Bump, bump, bump, bump, bump, bump.

(bounce up and down)

The people on the bus go bump, bump, bump,

Over the city streets.

HOLIDAYS

HOLIDAYS

Every year has days,

— and days,

— and days.

There are rainy days,

— and sunny days,

— and happy days.

There are days to play

— days to rest,

— but I like holidays the best.

HALLOWEEN

WITCH

If I were a witch,
(make high peaked hat, fingers touching high over head)

I'd ride on a broom
(one fist rides on top of other, waving through the air)

And scatter the ghosts,
(wave arms)

With a zoom, zoom, zoom.

SCARY EYES

See my big and scary eyes.
(circle thumb and index finger around eyes)

Look out now,

A big surprise — Boo!
(pull hands away, shout "Boo!")

HALLOWEEN WITCHES

One little, two little, three little witches,
(hold up one hand; nod fingers at each count)

Fly over haystacks,
(fly hand in up-down motion)

Fly over ditches,

Slide down moonbeams without any hitches.
(glide hand downward)

Heigh-ho! Halloween's here.

WITCH'S CAT

I am the witch's cat,
(make a fist with two fingers extended for cat)

Meow . . . . . . meow . . . . . .
(stroke fist with other hand)

My fur is black as night,

My eyes are green and bright.
(circle eyes with thumbs and forefingers)

I am the witch's cat,
(make a fist with two fingers extended and stroke fist with other hand)

Meow . . . . . . meow . . . . . .

MY PUMPKIN

See my pumpkin round and fat;
(make circle with hands, fingers spread wide, touching)

See my pumpkin yellow.
(make smaller circle)

Watch him grin on Halloween.
(point to mouth which is grinning wide)

He's a very funny fellow.

HALLOWEEN

Five little Jack-O-Lanterns,
(hold up five fingers)

Sitting on the gate.

This one said, "My, it is getting late!"
(use fingers)

This one said, "Who goes there?"

This one said, "Let's run, let's run!"

This one said, "Oh, no. It is only Halloween fun."

Along came the North Wind and blew out the light.

And away ran the Jack-O-Lanterns,
(fingers run away)

On Halloween night.

THE WITCH

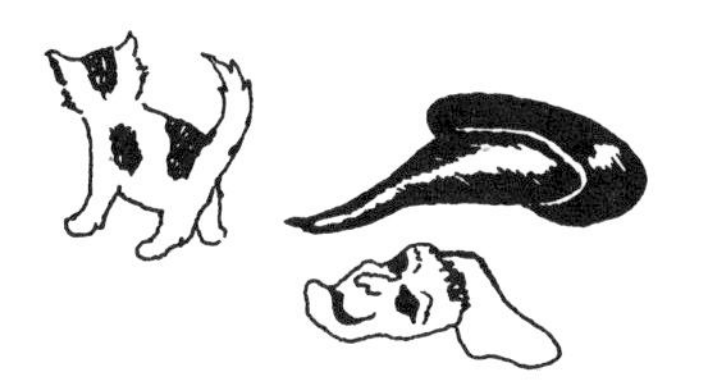

I saw a witch in a tall peaked hat,
(hands with fingers together on head, making a hat)

Riding a broom with a coal black cat!

I saw this witch, but she didn't see me,
(hand over eyes, looking)

For I was hiding behind a tree!
(arms close to body)

As she went by, I jumped out and called, "Boo!"

And my, she was frightened and away she flew!
(wave hands as if flying)

She left her broom and her tall peaked hat,
(make motions to portray hat on head)

Her painted mask and her coal black cat!

I don't know when I've had such fun,

As on Halloween night when I made a witch run!

THANKSGIVING

DAN TURKEY

I have a turkey,
(hold fingers together, extended forward touching thumb)

His name is Dan.

He has fine feathers,

That are colored tan.

He wobbles when he walks,
(walk hand)

And he gobbles when he talks,
(raise finger from thumb to "talk")

And he opens up his tail

Into a great big fan.
(hands together with fingers spread apart in fan position)

THANKSGIVING

I had a little turkey

And nothing would he say,

But gobble, gobble, gobble,
(move hands to show mouth moving)

All the live long day.

OUR TABLE

Every day when we eat
Our table is so small,
(make small circle with hands)
There's only room for daddy,
Mother, and me — that's all.
But Thanksgiving comes and the company!
You'd hardly believe your eyes!
That same table stretches — stretches,
(circle growing larger)
Until it is this size.
(open arms wide)

THE TURKEY AND THE PUMPKIN

"Thanksgiving Day is coming,"
So Mr. Turkey said.
"Now I must be real careful,
Or I shall lose my head."
(move finger across throat as though cutting)

The pumpkin heard the turkey,
"I'm frightened, too. Oh, my!
They'll mix me up with sugar and spice,
(move arm as though stirring)
And I'll be a pumpkin pie!"
(make large circle with hands)

THE TURKEY'S OPINION

"What do you think of drumsticks?"
I asked a barnyard bird.
He grinned a turkey grin, and then
He answered me this word.

"They're good to eat; they're good to beat,
(make appropriate motions for eating and beating)
But sure as I am living,
They're best to run away with
(fingers make running motions)
The week before Thanksgiving.

THANKSGIVING DAY

We are thankful for Thanksgiving Day,
We are thankful for sunshine, bright and fair.
(make round circle with hands)
We are thankful for nice, warm clothes to wear;
(point to clothes)
We are thankful for our family, kind and gay.
Yes, we are thankful for Thanksgiving Day!

CHRISTMAS

SANTA IS BACK

Two merry blue eyes,
(point to eyes)
A cute little nose,
(point to nose)
A long, snowy beard,
(make motion as if stroking beard)
Two cheeks like a rose,
A round, chubby form,
(make large circular motion around stomach)
A big bulging sack,
(shoulders bent, hands holding heavy sack)
Hurrah for old Santa!
(clap hands)
We're glad that he's back.

HERE IS THE CHIMNEY

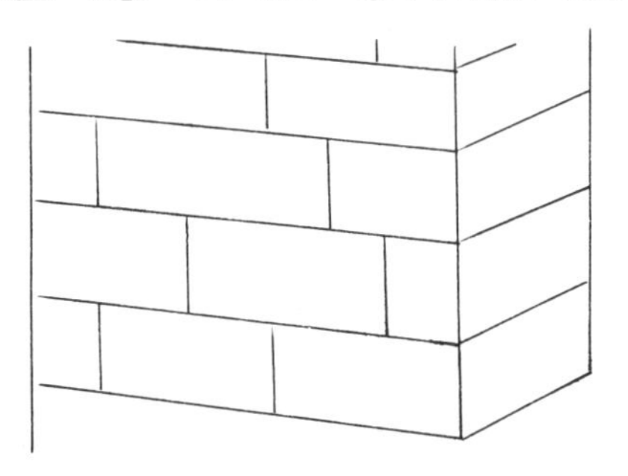

Here is the chimney,
(make fist, enclosing thumb)
Here is the top.
(place palm of other hand on top of fist)
Open the lid,
(remove top hand quickly)
And out Santa will pop.
(pop up thumb)

LITTLE JACK HORNER

Little Jack Horner
Sat in a corner
Eating his Christmas pie.
(cup hand to make pie, make eating motion with other hand)
He stuck in his thumb,
(insert thumb in fist)
And pulled out a plum,
(pull thumb out of fist and hold it up)
And said, "What a good boy am I."

A SHY SANTA

Isn't it the strangest thing
That Santa is so shy?
(hide face with hands)
We can never, never catch him,
No matter how we try.
(make fingers run)
It isn't any use to watch,
(hold hand over eyes and look all around)
Because my mother said,
"Santa Claus will only come
When children are in bed!"
(shake finger)

SANTA'S COMING

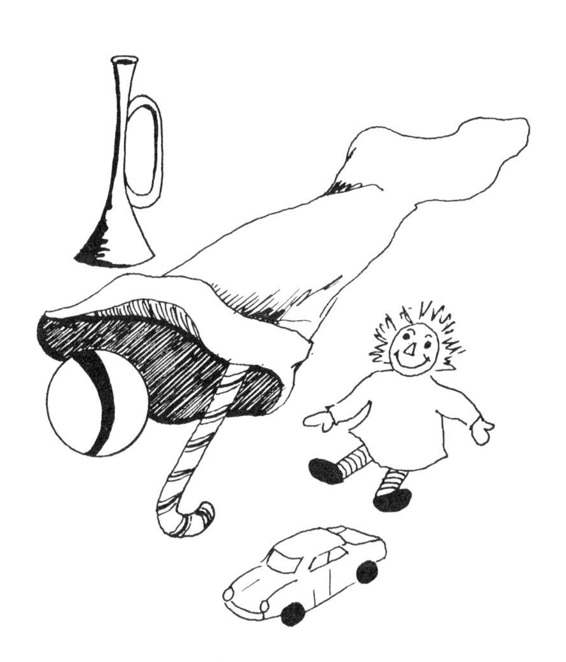

Santa's coming, Santa's coming!
I know what he'll bring.
Toys for you and toys for me,
Jingle, jangle, jing!

In my stocking I shall find
Oh, so many things,
Jack-in-the-box,
(right hand closed, thumb in, then out)
And a baby doll,
(arms cradling doll)
Jingle, jangle, jing!

A horn,
(both hands together at mouth)
A ball,
(make circle with finger tips)
And a candy cane,
(hand upright, fingers closed and dropping for the head of cane)
A puppet jumping on a string,
(hold hand up and pretend bouncing puppet tied to finger by string)

Oh, I'm glad it's Christmas time,
Jingle, jangle, jing!

CHRISTMAS IS A-COMING

Christmas is a-coming,

The geese are getting fat.
(pat tummy)

Please put a penny in the old man's hat.
(pretend to put penny in one palm)

If you haven't got a penny,

A ha' penny will do.
(tap palm)

God bless you.
(point to child)

SANTA CLAUS

Down the chimney old Santa Claus crept,
(fingers creep down)

Into the room where the children slept.

He saw their stockings hung in a row,
(suspend three fingers of left hand)

And he filled them with goodies from top to toe.
(make motions as if filling stockings)

Although he counted them — one, two, three,
(indicate by counting fingers)

The baby's stocking he could not see.

"Ho, ho," said Santa Claus, "that won't do."

So he popped her present right into her shoe.
(cup left hand and put finger of right hand into it)

FIVE RED STOCKINGS

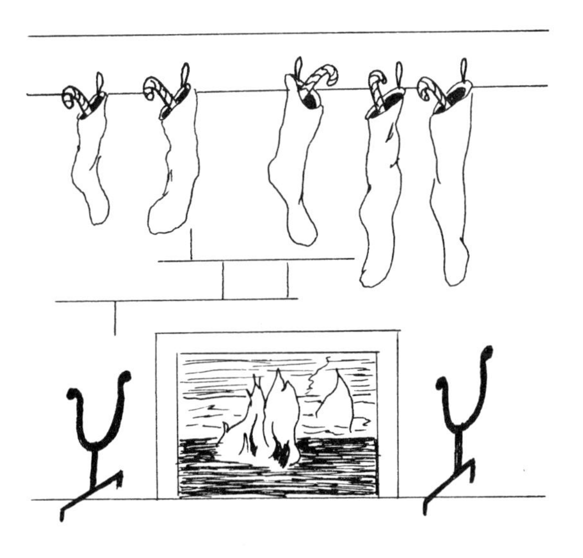

Five red stockings
(hold up five fingers)

Heard the fire roar.

________took one
(use child's name in the blanks)

Then there were four
(hold up four fingers)

Four red stockings

Saw the Christmas tree.

________took one

Then there were three.
(one finger down, leaving three up)

Three red stockings

Waiting for you.

________took one

Then there were two.
(another finger down, leaving two up)

Two red stockings

Having Christmas fun.

_________ took one

Then there was one.
(another finger down)

One red stocking

Feeling very gay.

_________ came along

And took it away.
(put hand behind back)